KU-041-995

leapfrog

Rhyme
Time

I Wish!

First published in 2008 by
Franklin Watts
338 Euston Road
London
NW1 3BH

Franklin Watts Australia
Level 17/207 Kent Street
Sydney
NSW 2000

Text © Sue Graves 2008
Illustration © Shelagh McNicholas 2008

The rights of Sue Graves to be identified as the author
and Shelagh McNicholas as the illustrator of this Work have
been asserted in accordance with the Copyright, Designs
and Patents Act, 1988.

All rights reserved. No part of this publication may be
reproduced, stored in a retrieval system, or transmitted
in any form or by any means, electronic, mechanical,
photocopy, recording or otherwise, without the prior
written permission of the copyright owner.

A CIP catalogue record for this book is available
from the British Library.

ISBN 978 0 7496 7940 8 (hbk)
ISBN 978 0 7496 7952 1 (pbk)

Series Editor: Jackie Hamley
Series Advisor: Dr Barrie Wade
Series Designer: Peter Scoulding

Printed in China

Franklin Watts is a division of
Hachette Children's Books,
an Hachette Livre UK company.

I Wish!

by Sue Graves

Illustrated by Shelagh McNicholas

W

FRANKLIN WATTS

LONDON • SYDNEY

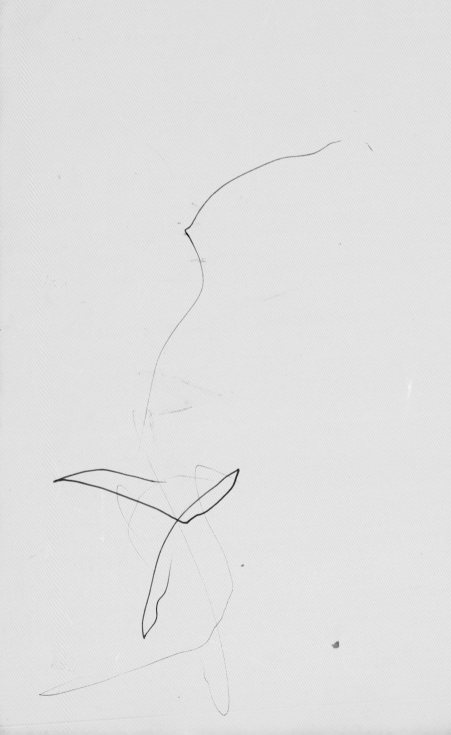

I wish I were a butterfly with brown and orange wings.

I'd flutter round the garden, collecting nectar and sweet things.

But what if it got chilly?
A butterfly can't wear
a vest.

I'm glad I'm not a butterfly.
A butterfly is not the best!

I wish I were a horrid witch
with a black and pointy hat.

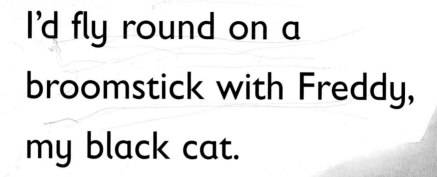

I'd fly round on a
broomstick with Freddy,
my black cat.

15

But it's quite spooky late at night.

There are bats and rats
and mice.

I'm glad I'm not
a horrid witch.
A witch is not so nice!

I wish I were a funny clown
with a red nose and a hat.

I'd play a lot of silly tricks
and flip like an acrobat.

But custard pies get
thrown at clowns!

They trickle down
your head!

I'm glad I'm not a
funny clown, but what
can I be instead?

It's hard to think of something that I would really like to be.

butterfly X
witch X
crown X

And when I really think about it ...

I'm very glad I'm me!

Leapfrog Rhyme Time has been specially designed to fit the requirements of the Literacy Framework. It offers real books for beginner readers by top authors and illustrators. There are 27 Leapfrog Rhyme Time stories to choose from:

* hardback